The family was going on holiday. They were taking Biff and Chip. Mum and Dad were busy packing the car.

"Will you pack these for us, please?" asked Wilma.

"There will be lots to do," said Dad.
"You won't need those."

"We will," said Wilf. "We must take the
games station. I've got a great new game."

"We want to watch these films," said
Wilma. "We haven't seen some of them
yet."

"And can we take the CD player?"
asked Biff.

It was a long journey. It took hours.
They stopped for a break.

"Let's get a drink," said Mum.

"Can we play a game in the arcade
first?" asked Wilf.

At last they arrived at the cottage.

"We're in the middle of a forest," said Wilf.

"We're in the middle of nowhere," said Wilma.

They went inside the cottage. Mum and
Dad began to unpack the car. There was a
big television in the front room.

"Great!" said Chip. "Let's watch TV."

"We could play some games," said Wilf.
"Could you bring in our games station,
Dad?"

"Not now," said Dad. "Come and help
us unpack the car."

At breakfast Wilma put on a film. Dad
sighed. "Get dressed everyone. We didn't
come on holiday to watch TV."

"Can we watch this first?" asked Wilma.

"Later," said Dad. "Let's go out."

"Wasn't it fun on the beach today?" said Mum.

But nobody said anything. Wilf and Biff were busy playing a game. Chip and Wilma were listening to a CD.

Suddenly all the lights went out. The
television and the CD player went off.

"What's happened?" called Biff.

Dad came in with a torch. "There's been
a power cut!" he said.

Mum found a lamp.

"What if the power doesn't come back on?" asked Chip, looking at the TV.

"We'll have to do without it," said Dad.

"Oh no!" said the children.

The power didn't come back on.
"It may be off for a long time," said Dad.
It was time to eat. They all sat round the
table and had supper by candlelight.

It was fun eating in the dark. They took
it in turns to tell stories. Dad told them a
funny story about a time when he was a
little boy. It made them all laugh.

That night the power didn't come back on. The children had to use the lamp to go to bed. Chip made a shadow on the wall with his hands.

"Guess what it is," he said.

Wilma shone a torch under her chin.
The light made her face look scary.
   "Whoooh!" she said. "I'm a monster."
Everyone laughed. Then Mum came in
and said it was time to go to sleep.

The next morning there was still no
power. So the family spent all day on the
beach. They played lots of games.

"It's late," said Mum. "It's time to go."

"Can't we stay a bit longer?" asked Wilf.

"I've got an idea," said Dad. "Let's
build a fire. We could cook supper."
"Brilliant!" they all shouted.
"Let's get some driftwood," said Mum.
"I'll go and get the food," said Dad.

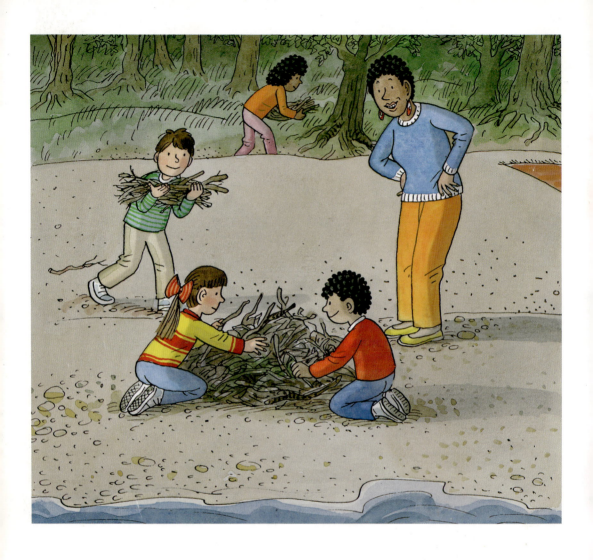

It was getting dark by the time the fire was finished.

"Hey Wilf! That looks like a giant bird's nest," said Mum. "You light it, not lay an egg in it!"

Dad cooked lots of food on the fire.
Then Mum toasted some marshmallows.
They all sat and looked at the stars.
    "I have a surprise," said Dad.
"Sparklers!"

"Sorry," said Dad the next morning.
"Still no power."

"We can do without it," smiled Chip.

"Last night was magic," said Wilf.

"What shall we do tonight?" asked Biff.

That night Wilma had a good idea.

"We could play hide and seek," she said.
"If you are 'It' you have a torch."

Everyone hid around the dark cottage.
Wilf was 'It'. He counted to a hundred.

Wilf looked in every room.

"Found you, Biff!" he called. Biff was hiding behind a big plant.

He found Chip lying in the bath. Wilma was behind the TV. Mum was under a bed.

But where was Dad? Suddenly, the moon came out from behind the clouds. It lit up the windows. Dad was hiding behind the curtains.

"That gives me an idea," thought Wilma.

The next day Biff, Chip and Wilf went
with Wilma to the woods.

"Why have we brought the boxes and a
sheet?" asked Chip.

"And why are we here so early?"
yawned Wilf.

"There's loads to do before tonight."
Wilma's eyes sparkled. "This evening, we
are going to do a shadow play!"

"Brilliant!" said Chip. "What's that?"

The children worked all day. They cut out shapes from the cardboard boxes. Wilf tied the sheet between two trees.

"What are you doing?" Dad asked.

"It's a surprise," said Wilma.

There was a golden sunset that evening.
The children had put down lots of candles
in jars.

"How beautiful!" said Mum.

"It's like magic!" gasped Dad.

Suddenly Biff turned up the lamp. The
sheet glowed. The play began. It was about
elves. The elves were cardboard puppets. Wilf
and Chip moved the puppets around.

Biff did the elves' voices. Wilma played
the guitar. They all sang songs. It was a
good story. It was funny and sad. It made
Mum laugh and Dad cry.

The play had finished. Everyone bowed.
"Hooray!" shouted Mum. "Well done!"
"Now," said Dad, "I've got a surprise."
"What is it?" asked Wilma.
"You'll see," smiled Dad.

They went back to the cottage. It was
pitch black.

"We can't see anything," said Wilf.

"I said 'you'll see' and now you can,"
said Dad. He turned on the power.

Dad laughed. "Surprise!" he said.
"I wanted you to enjoy the holiday without
TV. There was no power cut."

"Turn it off again," said the children.
"We can do without it."